ALICE
IN WONDERLAND

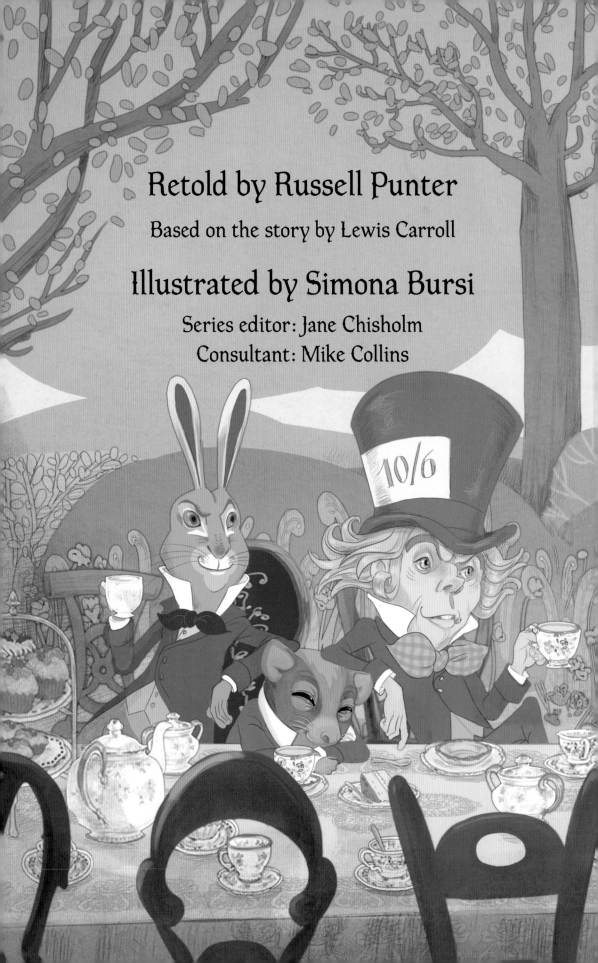

Retold by Russell Punter

Based on the story by Lewis Carroll

Illustrated by Simona Bursi

Series editor: Jane Chisholm
Consultant: Mike Collins

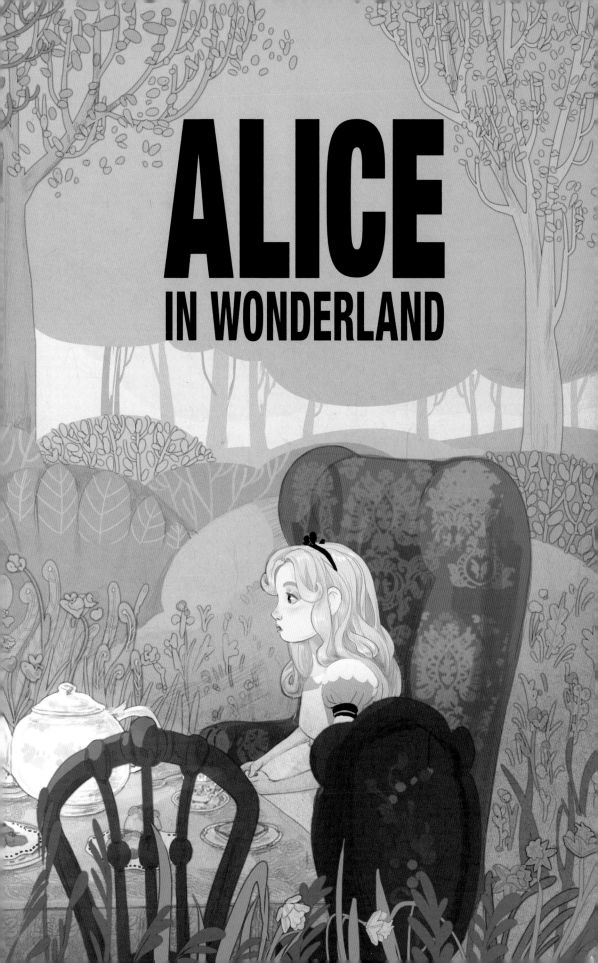

ALICE
IN WONDERLAND

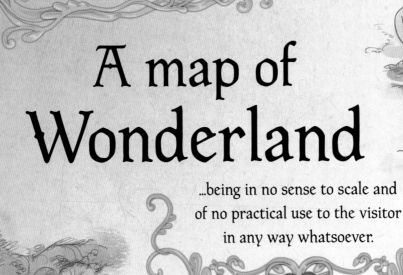

A map of Wonderland

...being in no sense to scale and
of no practical use to the visitor
in any way whatsoever.

The rabbit hole
& the well

The long hall

The Queen of
Hearts' garden

The pool of tears

The shore

The White
Rabbit's house

The Duchess's
house

The wood

The secret
door

The March
Hare's house

The croquet lawn

The Mock Turtle's
beach

The courthouse

Alice was beginning to get very tired of sitting by the riverbank. Alice's sister was engrossed in a book, with no pictures or conversations in it.

"What use is a book without pictures or conversations?" thought Alice.

The hot day was making Alice feel very sleepy. She was wondering whether the pleasure of making a daisy chain would be worth the trouble of getting up and picking the daisies, when suddenly, a white rabbit ran by...

I'VE **NEVER** SEEN A **RABBIT** WITH A **WAISTCOAT POCKET** – OR A **WATCH** TO TAKE OUT OF IT, COME TO THAT!

BURNING WITH CURIOSITY, ALICE RUNS ACROSS THE FIELD, AFTER THE WHITE RABBIT...

...JUST IN TIME TO SEE IT POP DOWN A RABBIT HOLE.

WITHOUT CONSIDERING HOW SHE MIGHT GET OUT, ALICE SQUEEZES IN AFTER THE RABBIT...

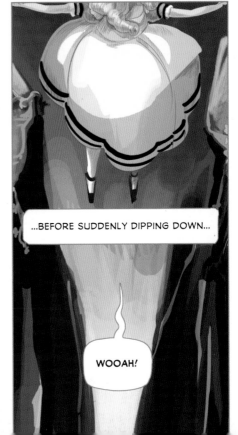

...BEFORE SUDDENLY DIPPING DOWN...

THE HOLE GOES STRAIGHT ON LIKE A TUNNEL...

WOOAH!

THEN, AT LAST...

THUMP!

OH MY **EARS** AND **WHISKERS**, HOW **LATE** IT'S GETTING!

ALICE FOLLOWS THE WHITE RABBIT DOWN THE PASSAGE.

BUT WHEN SHE TURNS THE CORNER...

HE'S **VANISHED!** HE **MUST** HAVE GONE THROUGH ONE OF THESE **DOORS!**

ALICE TRIES EACH DOOR IN TURN...

THEY'RE ALL **LOCKED!**

OH!

I'M SURE THAT TABLE WASN'T THERE **JUST NOW!**

ALICE TAKES THE TINY KEY FROM THE TABLE. BUT IT IS TOO SMALL TO FIT ANY OF THE LOCKS...

HMMM. I WONDER WHAT'S **BEHIND** THIS **CURTAIN**...

AH!

ALICE OPENS THE LITTLE DOOR AND PEEKS OUTSIDE...

WHAT A **LOVELY** GARDEN!

SHE LOCKS THE LITTLE DOOR AND SIGHS...

BUT EVEN IF MY **HEAD** COULD **GO THROUGH** THE **DOOR**, IT WOULD BE OF **LITTLE USE** WITHOUT MY **SHOULDERS**!

HOW I **WISH** I COULD **SHUT UP** LIKE A **TELESCOPE**!

WHEN ALICE TURNS TO PUT THE TINY KEY BACK ON THE GLASS TABLE...

OH!

DRINK ME

AFTER CHECKING THAT THE BOTTLE ISN'T MARKED 'POISON', ALICE TAKES A SIP OF THE CONTENTS...

MMMM, VERY NICE! IT TASTES RATHER LIKE CHERRY TART...

...AND CUSTARD...

...PINEAPPLE...

...ROAST TURKEY...

...TOFFEE...

...AND HOT BUTTERED TOAST!

WHAT A CURIOUS FEELING...

I MUST BE SHUTTING UP LIKE A TELESCOPE!

I HOPE I DON'T SHRINK ANY FURTHER...

...OR I MIGHT GO OUT LIKE A CANDLE!

NOW I SHALL BE **SMALL ENOUGH TO** FIT THROUGH THE **LITTLE DOOR...**

BUT...

OH NO! I **LEFT** THE **KEY** ON THE **TABLE.** NOW I'M TOO **TINY** TO **REACH** IT!

ALICE NOTICES A LITTLE GLASS BOX...

PERHAPS THERE'S **ANOTHER** KEY IN **THERE?**

A CAKE!

EAT ME

WELL, I'LL **EAT** IT, AND IF IT MAKES ME GROW **LARGER,** I CAN REACH THE KEY...

...IF IT MAKES ME GROW **SMALLER,** I CAN CREEP UNDER THE DOOR.

SO **EITHER** WAY, I'LL GET INTO THE GARDEN, AND I DON'T CARE **WHAT** HAPPENS!

ALICE BEGINS TO SOB...

YOU OUGHT TO BE **ASHAMED** OF YOURSELF, A **GREAT GIRL** LIKE YOU, TO GO ON **CRYING** IN THIS WAY!

STOP THIS **MOMENT**, I TELL YOU!

BUT ALICE GOES ON ALL THE SAME, SHEDDING GALLONS OF TEARS...

AFTER A TIME, SHE HEARS THE PATTERING OF FEET...

OH! THE **DUCHESS**, THE **DUCHESS**!

OH, WON'T SHE BE **SAVAGE** IF I'VE KEPT HER **WAITING**!

IF YOU **PLEASE**, SIR...

THE STARTLED WHITE RABBIT DASHES OFF, DROPPING HIS FAN AND GLOVES...

DEAR, DEAR! HOW **QUEER** EVERYTHING IS TODAY! **YESTERDAY,** THINGS WENT ON **JUST AS USUAL!**

I WONDER IF I'VE BEEN **CHANGED** INTO SOMEONE I **KNOW** DURING THE NIGHT?

I'M SURE I CAN'T BE **ADA,** FOR HER **HAIR** GOES IN **LONG RINGLETS!**

AND I'M SURE I CAN'T BE **MABEL,** FOR I KNOW **ALL SORTS** OF THINGS AND SHE KNOWS **VERY LITTLE!**

I KNOW THAT FOUR TIMES FIVE IS **TWELVE,** AND FOUR TIMES SIX IS **THIRTEEN,** AND FOUR TIMES SEVEN IS... **OH DEAR!**

LONDON IS THE CAPITAL OF **PARIS,** AND PARIS IS THE CAPITAL OF **ROME,** AND ROME... NO, THAT'S **ALL WRONG!**

I'LL TRY TO SAY THE POEM, '*HOW DOTH THE LITTLE BUSY BEE*'...

HOW DOTH THE LITTLE CROCODILE IMPROVE HIS SHINING TAIL, AND POUR THE WATERS OF THE NILE ON EVERY GOLDEN SCALE!

HOW CHEERFULLY HE SEEMS TO GRIN, HOW NEATLY SPREADS HIS CLAWS, AND WELCOMES LITTLE FISHES IN WITH GENTLY SMILING JAWS!

I'M SURE *THOSE* WEREN'T THE RIGHT WORDS!

ALICE SUDDENLY REALIZES THAT SHE'S PUT ON ONE OF THE WHITE RABBIT'S GLOVES...

HOW *CAN* I HAVE DONE **THAT?** I MUST BE GROWING **SMALL** AGAIN.

SHE REMOVES THE GLOVE, BUT KEEPS SHRINKING...

...**TOO** SMALL! PERHAPS THE WHITE RABBIT'S **FAN** IS THE CAUSE...

ALICE DROPS THE FAN, JUST IN TIME TO STOP HERSELF FROM SHRINKING AWAY ALTOGETHER...

THAT WAS A **NARROW ESCAPE!**

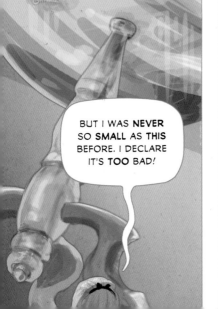

BUT I WAS **NEVER** SO **SMALL** AS THIS BEFORE. I DECLARE IT'S **TOO** BAD!

WHOOPS!

SPLASH!

ALL MUST HAVE **PRIZES!**

BUT **WHO** IS TO **GIVE** THE PRIZES?

PRIZES!

WHY, **SHE**, OF COURSE!

PRIZES!

PRIZES!

PRIZES!

ALICE PUTS HER HAND IN HER POCKET AND PULLS OUT A BOX OF SUGAR-COATED NUTS...

THERE'S **JUST** ENOUGH FOR **ONE** EACH!

BUT **YOU** MUST HAVE A PRIZE **YOURSELF!**

THE ONLY OTHER THING I HAVE IS THIS **THIMBLE!**

THE DODO TAKES THE THIMBLE FROM ALICE, THEN SOLEMNLY OFFERS IT BACK...

WE **BEG** YOUR **ACCEPTANCE** OF THIS **ELEGANT** THIMBLE!

HOORAY!

COME AWAY, MY DEARS! IT'S HIGH TIME YOU WERE BOTH IN BED!

I REALLY MUST BE GETTING HOME!

ONE BY ONE, ALL THE ANIMALS SCURRY AWAY...

I WISH I HADN'T MENTIONED DINAH! THOUGH I'M SURE SHE'S THE BEST CAT IN THE WORLD.

OH, MY DEAR DINAH! I WONDER IF I SHALL EVER SEE YOU AGAIN?

AS ALICE BEGINS TO CRY, SHE HEARS THE PATTERING OF FOOTSTEPS...

THE DUCHESS! THE DUCHESS! OH MY DEAR PAWS! OH MY FUR AND WHISKERS!

SHE'LL GET ME EXECUTED, AS SURE AS FERRETS ARE FERRETS!

WHERE CAN I HAVE DROPPED THEM, I WONDER?

THE WHITE RABBIT SUDDENLY NOTICES HE'S NOT ALONE...

WHY, **MARY ANN**, WHAT ARE **YOU** DOING **OUT HERE**?

BE A GOOD **HOUSEMAID** – RUN **HOME** THIS MOMENT, AND FETCH ME A PAIR OF **GLOVES** AND A **FAN!** QUICK NOW!

WITHOUT TRYING TO EXPLAIN THE MISTAKE THE WHITE RABBIT HAS MADE, ALICE RUNS OFF IN THE DIRECTION HE INDICATED...

HE MISTOOK ME FOR HIS **HOUSEMAID!**

HOW **QUEER** IT SEEMS, TO BE TAKING **ORDERS** FROM A **RABBIT!**

STILL, I'D BETTER TAKE HIM HIS **FAN** AND **GLOVES**... THAT IS, IF I CAN **FIND** THEM!

ALICE SOON COMES TO A NEAT LITTLE HOUSE...

White Rabbit

ALICE GOES INSIDE AND CLIMBS THE STAIRS TO A TIDY LITTLE ROOM...

SHE PICKS UP A FAN AND A PAIR OF GLOVES FROM THE TABLE AND IS ABOUT TO LEAVE, WHEN SHE NOTICES A LITTLE BOTTLE...

I KNOW **SOMETHING** INTERESTING IS SURE TO HAPPEN WHENEVER I **EAT** OR **DRINK** ANYTHING...

...SO I'LL JUST **SEE** WHAT **THIS** BOTTLE **DOES!**

I **DO** HOPE IT'LL MAKE ME GROW **LARGE** AGAIN, FOR I'M REALLY QUITE **TIRED** OF BEING SUCH A **TINY** THING!

BEFORE ALICE HAS DRUNK HALF THE BOTTLE...

THAT'S QUITE **ENOUGH!**

I HOPE I SHAN'T **GROW** ANY **MORE!** AS IT **IS,** I CAN'T GET **OUT** OF THE **DOOR!**

BUT ALICE KEEPS GROWING...

...AND GROWING...

...AND GROWING...

JUST AS ALICE FINALLY STOPS GROWING, SHE HEARS A FAMILIAR VOICE OUTSIDE THE DOOR...

MARY ANN! MARY ANN! FETCH ME MY GLOVES THIS MOMENT!

OH NO! THE WHITE RABBIT WILL BE FURIOUS! I CAN'T LET HIM SEE ME!

THE DOOR'S STUCK! I'LL GO OUTSIDE AND GET IN AT A WINDOW!

OH NO, YOU WON'T!

THE WHITE RABBIT CLIMBS UP TO A WINDOW...

BUT ALICE IS READY FOR HIM...

SHRIEK!

SNATCH!

AN **ARM**, YOU GOOSE! WHO EVER SAW ONE THAT SIZE?

WHY, IT **FILLS** THE **WHOLE WINDOW**!

IT CERTAINLY **DOES**, SIR. BUT IT'S **STILL** AN ARM!

WELL, IT'S GOT **NO BUSINESS** THERE, AT ANY RATE.

GO AND **TAKE IT AWAY!**

SNATCH!

SHRIEK!

SHRIEK!

CRASH!

ALICE WAITS FOR SOME TIME WITHOUT HEARING ANYTHING MORE. THEN COME THE SOUNDS OF A SQUEAKY WHEELBARROW AND LOTS OF RAISED VOICES...

HERE, **BILL!** THE MASTER SAYS YOU'VE GOT TO GO DOWN THE **CHIMNEY!**

WILL THE ROOF **TAKE** IT?

HERE, **BILL!** CATCH HOLD OF THIS **ROPE!**

MIND THAT **LOOSE SLATE!**

OH! SO **BILL'S** COMING DOWN THE **CHIMNEY**, IS HE?

THIS **FIREPLACE** IS **NARROW**, BUT I *THINK* I CAN **KICK** A LITTLE!

WOOOAAH!

CRUNCH!

I **WONDER** WHAT THEY'LL DO **NEXT**?

IF THEY HAD ANY **SENSE**, THEY'D TAKE THE **ROOF OFF**.

AFTER A MINUTE OR TWO...

THERE GOES BILL!

CATCH HIM BY THE **HEDGE!**

A **BARROWFUL** WILL **DO**, TO **BEGIN** WITH!

A **BARROWFUL** OF *WHAT?*

...AND KEEPS RUNNING UNTIL SHE FINDS HERSELF SAFE IN DENSE UNDERGROWTH...

THE **FIRST** THING I'VE GOT TO DO IS TO GROW TO MY **RIGHT SIZE** AGAIN...

...THE **SECOND** THING IS TO FIND MY WAY INTO THAT **LOVELY GARDEN.**

BUT HOW AM I TO **MANAGE** GETTING BACK TO MY **RIGHT SIZE?**

...BUT THE GREAT QUESTION IS **WHAT?**

I SUPPOSE I OUGHT TO **EAT** OR **DRINK** SOMETHING OR OTHER...

ALICE LOOKS ALL AROUND HER AT THE FLOWERS AND BLADES OF GRASS...

BUT SHE CAN'T SEE ANYTHING THAT MAY HELP.

THEN SHE COMES TO A LARGE MUSHROOM...

SHE STRETCHES HERSELF ON TIPTOE AND PEERS OVER THE EDGE...

GASP!

NOT A BIT!

WELL, PERHAPS *YOUR* FEELINGS MAY BE **DIFFERENT**. ALL I KNOW IS, IT WOULD FEEL **VERY QUEER** TO *ME!*

YOU! WHO ARE *YOU?*

I THINK YOU OUGHT TO TELL ME WHO *YOU* ARE **FIRST!**

WHY?

TIRED BY ALL THE CATERPILLAR'S PUZZLING QUESTIONS, ALICE WALKS AWAY...

COME BACK! I'VE SOMETHING **IMPORTANT** TO SAY...

...KEEP YOUR **TEMPER!**

IS THAT **ALL?**

NO...

THE CATERPILLAR PUFFS ON HIS PIPE FOR A FEW MINUTES, BEFORE CONTINUING...

SO YOU THINK YOU'RE **CHANGED,** DO YOU?

I'M AFRAID I **AM,** SIR. I CAN'T **REMEMBER** THINGS AS I **USED,** AND I DON'T **KEEP THE SAME** SIZE FOR TEN MINUTES TOGETHER*!*

CAN'T REMEMBER *WHAT* THINGS?

WELL, I **TRIED** TO SAY *'HOW DOTH THE LITTLE BUSY BEE',* BUT IT ALL CAME OUT **DIFFERENT!**

REPEAT *'YOU ARE OLD FATHER WILLIAM'.*

"You are old, father William," the young man said,
"And your hair has become very white;
And yet you incessantly stand on your head –
Do you think, at your age, it is right?"

"In my youth," father William replied to his son,
"I feared it might injure the brain;
But now that I'm perfectly sure I have none,
Why, I do it again and again."

"You are old," said the youth, "as I mentioned before,
And have grown most uncommonly fat;
Yet you turned a back-somersault in at the door –
Pray, what is the reason of that?"

"In my youth," said the sage, as he shook his grey locks,
"I kept all my limbs very supple
By use of this ointment – one shilling the box –
Allow me to sell you a couple."

"You are old," said the youth, "and your jaws are too weak
For anything tougher than suet;
Yet you finished the goose, with the bones and the beak –
Pray, how did you manage to do it?"

"In my youth," said his father, "I took to the law,
And argued each case with my wife;
And the muscular strength, which it gave to my jaw,
Has lasted the rest of my life."

"You are old," said the youth; "one would hardly suppose
That your eye was as steady as ever;
Yet you balanced an eel on the end of your nose –
What made you so awfully clever?"

"I have answered three questions, and that is enough,"
Said his father; "don't give yourself airs!
Do you think I can listen all day to such stuff?
Be off, or I'll kick you down stairs!"

ALICE STRETCHES HER ARMS AROUND THE MUSHROOM, AND BREAKS OFF A BIT OF THE EDGE WITH EACH HAND...

AND NOW **WHICH** IS **WHICH**?

ALICE TRIES THE FIRST PIECE...

OH **DEAR!**

I'LL TRY THIS **OTHER** PIECE!

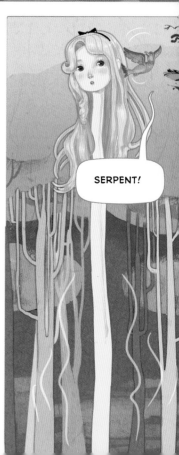

SERPENT!

SPEAK ROUGHLY TO YOUR LITTLE BOY,
AND BEAT HIM WHEN HE SNEEZES;
HE ONLY DOES IT TO ANNOY,
BECAUSE HE KNOWS IT TEASES.

WOW! WOW! WOW!

I SPEAK SEVERELY TO MY BOY,
I BEAT HIM WHEN HE SNEEZES;
FOR HE CAN THOROUGHLY ENJOY
THE PEPPER WHEN HE PLEASES!

WOW! WOW! WOW!

HERE! YOU MAY
NURSE IT A BIT,
IF YOU LIKE!

THUD!

WHIZZ!

I MUST GO AND
GET READY TO
PLAY CROQUET
WITH THE QUEEN!

ALICE WALKS ON IN THE DIRECTION IN WHICH THE MARCH HARE IS SAID TO LIVE...

I'VE SEEN HATTERS **BEFORE**. THE **MARCH HARE** WILL BE **MUCH** THE **MORE INTERESTING**...

...AND PERHAPS, AS THIS IS **MAY**, IT WON'T BE **RAVING MAD**, AT LEAST NOT **SO** MAD AS IT WAS IN **MARCH**!

SHE LOOKS UP TO SEE THE CAT AGAIN...

DID YOU SAY **PIG**, OR **FIG**?

I SAID PIG.

AND I WISH YOU WOULDN'T KEEP **APPEARING** AND **VANISHING** SO **SUDDENLY**. YOU MAKE ME QUITE **GIDDY**!

ALL RIGHT!

WELL! I'VE OFTEN SEEN A **CAT** WITHOUT A GRIN, BUT A *GRIN* WITHOUT A *CAT*?!

IT'S THE MOST **CURIOUS** THING I EVER SAW IN ALL MY **LIFE**!

HAVING NIBBLED ENOUGH OF THE CATERPILLAR'S MUSHROOM TO GROW TO TWO FEET TALL, ALICE CARRIES ON WALKING UNTIL SHE COMES TO THE MARCH HARE'S HOUSE.

IT **WAS** THE **BEST** BUTTER!

YES, BUT SOME **CRUMBS** MUST HAVE GOT IN AS WELL.

YOU SHOULDN'T HAVE PUT IT IN WITH THE **BREAD KNIFE**!

SPLOSH!

IT **WAS** THE **BEST** BUTTER, YOU KNOW!

THE DORMOUSE IS **ASLEEP** AGAIN!

SPLISH!

OF **COURSE**, JUST WHAT I WAS GOING TO REMARK **MYSELF**!

HAVE YOU **GUESSED** THE **RIDDLE** YET?

NO, I **GIVE UP**. WHAT'S THE ANSWER?

I HAVEN'T THE **SLIGHTEST IDEA**!

NOR I!

I THINK YOU MIGHT DO SOMETHING **BETTER** WITH THE **TIME**, THAN **WASTING** IT IN ASKING **RIDDLES** THAT HAVE **NO ANSWERS**.

IS THAT THE WAY *YOU* MANAGE?

NOT I! TIME AND I QUARRELLED LAST MARCH, JUST BEFORE THE MARCH HARE WENT MAD...

IT WAS AT THE GREAT CONCERT GIVEN BY THE QUEEN OF HEARTS, AND I HAD TO SING...

TWINKLE, TWINKLE, LITTLE BAT! HOW I WONDER WHAT YOU'RE AT!

UP ABOVE THE WORLD YOU FLY, LIKE A TEA-TRAY IN THE SKY. TWINKLE, TWINKLE...

TWINKLE, TWINKLE, TWINKLE, TWINKLE...

WELL, I'D HARDLY FINISHED THE FIRST VERSE, WHEN THE QUEEN BAWLED OUT "HE'S MURDERING TIME! OFF WITH HIS HEAD!"

HOW DREADFULLY SAVAGE!

AND EVER SINCE THAT, TIME WON'T DO ANYTHING I ASK! IT'S ALWAYS SIX O'CLOCK NOW.

IS THAT THE REASON SO MANY TEA-THINGS ARE PUT OUT HERE?

YES, THAT'S IT. IT'S ALWAYS TEATIME, AND WE'VE NO TIME TO WASH THE CROCKERY!

THEN YOU KEEP MOVING ROUND, I SUPPOSE?

IGNORING THIS, ALICE REPEATS HER QUESTION...

WHY DID THEY LIVE AT THE BOTTOM OF THE **WELL?**

IT WAS A **TREACLE** WELL.

THERE'S NO **SUCH** THING!

SSSHHH!

AND SO THESE THREE LITTLE SISTERS WERE LEARNING TO **DRAW...**

WHAT DID THEY DRAW?

TREACLE!

I WANT A **CLEAN CUP.** LET'S ALL MOVE **ONE PLACE ON!**

AFTER THEY'VE ALL CHANGED SEATS...

I DON'T UNDERSTAND. WHERE DID THE SISTERS DRAW THE TREACLE **FROM?**

FROM THE **WELL,** STUPID!

ALICE SUDDENLY NOTICES THAT ONE OF THE TREES HAS A DOOR...

THAT'S VERY **CURIOUS!** BUT **EVERYTHING'S** CURIOUS **TODAY!**

I MAY AS WELL GO IN.

TO HER SURPRISE, SHE FINDS HERSELF BACK IN THE LONG HALL...

I'LL MANAGE **BETTER** THIS TIME...

JUST TALL ENOUGH TO REACH THE LITTLE GOLDEN KEY ON THE GLASS TABLE, ALICE UNLOCKS THE DOOR TO THE GARDEN...

THEN SHE TAKES A BITE FROM THE CATERPILLAR'S MUSHROOM...

...AND WALKS INTO THE GARDEN...

YOU *SHAN'T* BE BEHEADED!

WHILE THE SOLDIERS ESCORT THE QUEEN'S GUESTS TO THE CROQUET LAWN, ALICE HIDES THE GARDENERS...

WHEN THE SOLDIERS RETURN...

?

?

?

NOW, CAN YOU PLAY **CROQUET**?

YES!

COME ON THEN!

ALICE JOINS THE PROCESSION TO THE CROQUET LAWN...

IT'S A VERY **FINE** DAY!

VERY. WHERE'S THE **DUCHESS?**

HUSH! HUSH!

SHE'S UNDER SENTENCE OF EXECUTION!

WHAT FOR?

DID YOU SAY 'WHAT A PITY'?

NO, I DIDN'T. I DON'T THINK IT'S A **PITY** AT ALL!

I SAID, 'WHAT FOR?'

SHE **BOXED** THE QUEEN'S EARS...

HA HA!

OH, **HUSH!** THE QUEEN WILL **HEAR** YOU!

YOU SEE, THE **DUCHESS** CAME RATHER **LATE**, AND THE **QUEEN** SAID...

GET TO YOUR PLACES!

THE GAME QUICKLY GETS UNDER WAY. BUT IT'S UNLIKE ANY CROQUET MATCH ALICE HAS EVER SEEN...

THE PLAYERS ALL PLAY AT ONCE, WITHOUT WAITING FOR TURNS...

THE 'HOOPS' KEEP GETTING UP...

THE HEDGEHOG 'BALLS' UNROLL...

IT MAY **KISS** MY **HAND** IF IT LIKES.

I'D RATHER **NOT**.

DON'T BE **IMPERTINENT!** AND DON'T **LOOK** AT ME LIKE THAT!

A **CAT** MAY LOOK AT A **KING**.

I READ THAT IN A **BOOK**, BUT I DON'T REMEMBER **WHERE**.

MY **DEAR!** I WISH YOU WOULD HAVE THIS CAT **REMOVED!**

OFF WITH HIS HEAD!

CHIEF EXECUTIONER – **ATTEND TO IT!**

BUT AT THAT VERY MOMENT, THE CHESHIRE CAT VANISHES INTO THIN AIR...

YOU CAN'T **CUT** OFF A HEAD UNLESS THERE'S A **BODY** TO CUT IT OFF **FROM!**

I'VE NEVER HAD TO DO SUCH A THING **BEFORE**, AND I'M NOT GOING TO BEGIN AT **MY** TIME OF LIFE!

DON'T TALK **NONSENSE**. ANYTHING THAT HAS A **HEAD** CAN BE BEHEADED!

IF **SOMETHING** ISN'T DONE ABOUT IT IN LESS THAN NO TIME, I'LL HAVE **EVERYBODY** EXECUTED!

HAVE YOU SEEN THE **MOCK TURTLE** YET?

NO. I DON'T **EVEN** KNOW WHAT A MOCK TURTLE **IS!**

IT'S THE THING **MOCK TURTLE SOUP** IS MADE FROM.

I NEVER **SAW** OR **HEARD** OF ONE.

COME ON, THEN, AND HE SHALL **TELL YOU** HIS **HISTORY.**

THEY VERY SOON COME UPON A GRYPHON LYING FAST ASLEEP IN THE SUN...

UP, LAZY THING!

TAKE THIS YOUNG LADY TO SEE THE **MOCK TURTLE** TO HEAR HIS **HISTORY.**

I MUST GO BACK AND SEE ABOUT SOME **EXECUTIONS** I'VE ORDERED.

IT'S ALL HER **FANCY**, THAT. THEY **NEVER EXECUTES NOBODY,** YOU KNOW.

COME ON!

AND HOW MANY **HOURS** A DAY DID YOU DO **LESSONS?**

TEN HOURS THE **FIRST** DAY, **NINE** THE **NEXT**, AND SO ON.

WHAT A **CURIOUS** PLAN!

THAT'S THE REASON THEY'RE CALLED **LESSONS**, BECAUSE THEY **LESSEN** FROM DAY TO DAY.

THEN THE **ELEVENTH** DAY MUST HAVE BEEN A **HOLIDAY?**

OF **COURSE** IT WAS.

AND HOW DID YOU MANAGE ON THE **TWELFTH?**

THAT'S **ENOUGH** ABOUT **LESSONS!** TELL HER SOMETHING ABOUT THE **GAMES** NOW.

YOU MAY NOT HAVE LIVED MUCH **UNDER** THE **SEA**, AND PERHAPS YOU WERE NEVER INTRODUCED TO A **LOBSTER**...

I ONCE **TASTED**... ER, NO, NEVER!

...SO YOU CAN HAVE **NO IDEA** WHAT A **DELIGHTFUL** THING A **LOBSTER-QUADRILLE** IS!

IT MUST BE A VERY **PRETTY** DANCE.

WOULD YOU LIKE TO **SEE A LITTLE** OF IT?

VERY MUCH INDEED.

COME, LET'S TRY THE **FIRST FIGURE!** WE CAN DO WITHOUT **LOBSTERS.**

WHAT SHALL WE **SING?**

OH, **YOU** SING. I'VE **FORGOTTEN** THE **WORDS.**

"Will you walk a little faster?"
said a whiting to a snail.
"There's a porpoise close behind us,
and he's treading on my tail.
See how eagerly the lobsters
and the turtles all advance!
They are waiting on the shingle –
will you come and join the dance?
Will you, won't you, will you, won't you,
will you join the dance?
Will you, won't you, will you, won't you,
won't you join the dance?

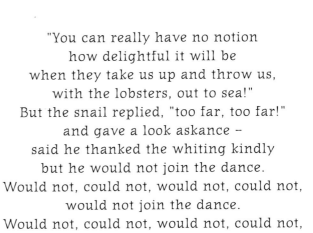

"You can really have no notion
how delightful it will be
when they take us up and throw us,
with the lobsters, out to sea!"
But the snail replied, "too far, too far!"
and gave a look askance –
said he thanked the whiting kindly
but he would not join the dance.
Would not, could not, would not, could not,
would not join the dance.
Would not, could not, would not, could not,
could not join the dance.

THANK YOU, IT'S A VERY **INTERESTING** DANCE TO WATCH.

SHALL WE TRY **ANOTHER** FIGURE, OR WOULD YOU LIKE THE **MOCK TURTLE** TO **SING** YOU A **SONG**?

OH, A **SONG** PLEASE, IF THE **MOCK TURTLE** WOULD BE SO **KIND**.

HM*!* NO ACCOUNTING FOR **TASTES***!* SING HER *'TURTLE SOUP'* WILL YOU, OLD FELLOW?

Beautiful soup, so rich and green,
Waiting in a hot tureen!
Who for such dainties would not stoop?
Soup of the evening, beautiful soup!
Soup of the evening, beautiful soup!
Beau-ootiful soo-oop!
Beau-ootiful soo-oop!
Soo-oop of the e-e-evening,
Beautiful, beautiful soup!

AS THE MOCK TURTLE FINISHES, A CRY COMES FROM THE DISTANCE...

THE TRIAL'S BEGINNING*!*

COME ON*!*

WHAT **TRIAL** IS IT?

COME ON*!*

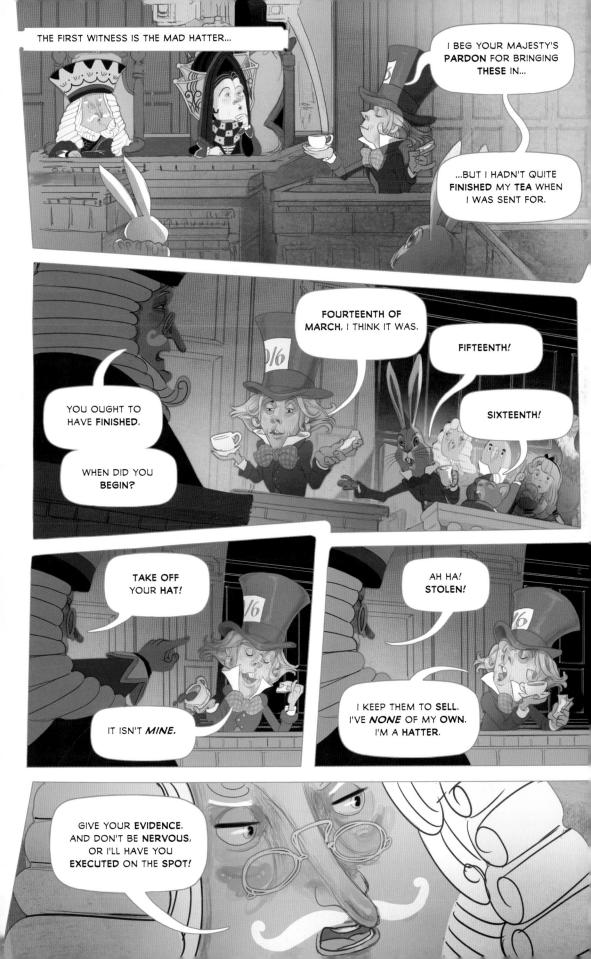

I WISH YOU WOULDN'T **SQUEEZE** SO. I CAN HARDLY **BREATHE!**

I CAN'T **HELP** IT. I'M **GROWING!**

YOU'VE **NO RIGHT** TO GROW *HERE!*

DON'T TALK **NONSENSE.** YOU KNOW **YOU'RE** GROWING **TOO.**

YES, BUT I GROW AT A **REASONABLE PACE.** NOT IN THAT **RIDICULOUS** FASHION!

MEANWHILE, THE KING IS GETTING IMPATIENT WITH THE HATTER...

GIVE YOUR **EVIDENCE** OR I'LL HAVE YOU **EXECUTED,** WHETHER YOU'RE **NERVOUS** OR **NOT!**

I'M A **POOR** MAN, YOUR MAJESTY, AND I'D JUST BEGUN MY **TEA,** AND WHAT WITH THE **BREAD AND BUTTER** GETTING SO **THIN** AND THE **TWINKLING** OF THE **TEA...**

THE **TWINKLING** OF THE **WHAT?**

IT *BEGAN* WITH THE **TEA.**

OF COURSE **TWINKLING** BEGINS WITH A **T!** DO YOU TAKE ME FOR A **DUNCE?**

GO ON!

I'M A **POOR** MAN AND MOST THINGS **TWINKLED** AFTER **THAT**, ONLY THE **MARCH HARE** SAID...

I DIDN'T!

YOU **DID**!

I DENY IT!

HE **DENIES** IT. **LEAVE OUT** THAT PART!

WELL, AT ANY RATE, THE **DORMOUSE** SAID...

AFTER **THAT**, I CUT SOME **MORE** BREAD AND BUTTER...

BUT WHAT DID THE **DORMOUSE** SAY?

THAT I CAN'T REMEMBER.

YOU **MUST** REMEMBER, OR I'LL HAVE YOU **EXECUTED**!

I'M A **POOR** MAN, YOUR MAJESTY...

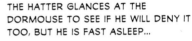

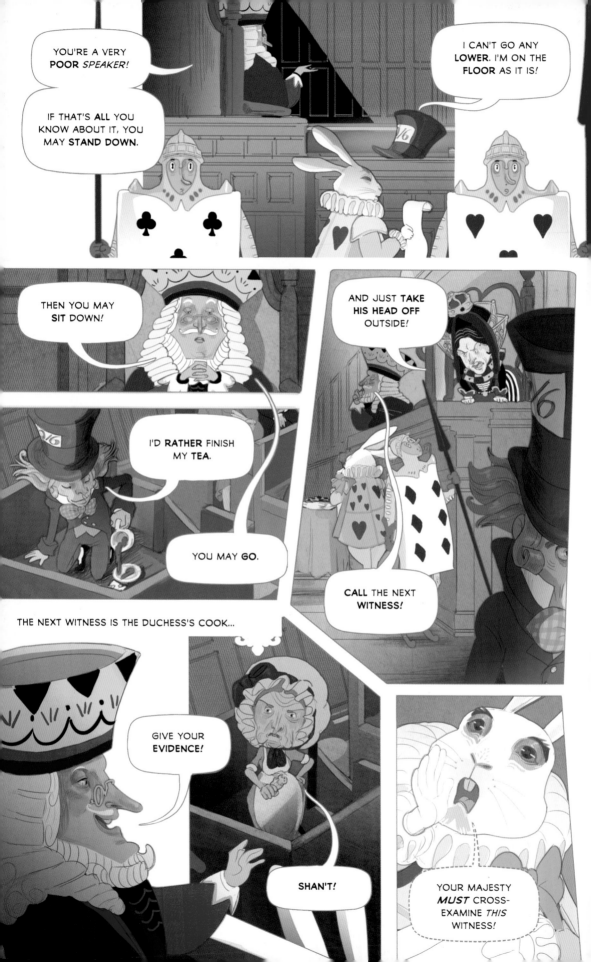

WELL, IF I **MUST**, I **MUST**.

PEPPER, MOSTLY.

TREACLE!

WHAT ARE **TARTS** MADE OF?

BEHEAD THAT **DORMOUSE!**

TURN THAT DORMOUSE **OUT** OF COURT!

SUPPRESS HIM! PINCH HIM!

OFF WITH HIS **WHISKERS!**

BY THE TIME THE DORMOUSE HAS BEEN TURNED OUT OF THE COURT, THE COOK HAS DISAPPEARED...

REALLY, MY DEAR, *YOU* MUST CROSS-EXAMINE THE **NEXT** WITNESS.

IT **QUITE** MAKES MY **FOREHEAD** ACHE!

CALL THE **NEXT WITNESS!**

ALICE!

HERE!

ALICE RUSHES FROM THE GALLERY, BUT, FORGETTING HER NEW SIZE, SHE TRIPS...

WHOOPS!

...AND TIPS OVER THE JURORS' STAND...

HELP!

WAAH!

WOOAH!

ALICE PICKS UP THE JURORS AS QUICKLY AS SHE CAN...

OH, I DO BEG YOUR PARDON!

THE TRIAL CANNOT PROCEED UNTIL ALL THE JURORS ARE BACK IN THEIR PROPER PLACES!

AFTER ALICE HAS SORTED OUT THE MESS...

WHAT DO YOU **KNOW** ABOUT **THIS** BUSINESS?

NOTHING.

NOTHING **WHATEVER?**

NOTHING WHATEVER.

THAT'S VERY **IMPORTANT!**

UNIMPORTANT, YOUR MAJESTY MEANS, OF COURSE.

UNIMPORTANT, I MEANT, OF COURSE.

THE KING CONSULTS HIS RULE BOOK...

RULE FORTY-TWO. ALL PERSONS **MORE** THAN A **MILE HIGH** TO **LEAVE** THE **COURT!**

I'M NOT **A MILE HIGH!**

YOU ARE!

NEARLY **TWO** MILES HIGH!

WELL, I **SHAN'T** GO, AT ANY RATE.

BESIDES, THAT'S NOT A **REGULAR** RULE. YOU **INVENTED** IT **JUST NOW!**

IT'S THE **OLDEST** RULE IN THE **BOOK!**

THEN IT **OUGHT** TO BE **NUMBER ONE!**

SCRIBBLE!

SCRIBBLE!

CONSIDER YOUR **VERDICT!**

THERE'S **MORE** EVIDENCE TO COME, **YET**, YOUR MAJESTY.

AS ALICE SAYS THESE WORDS, THE WHOLE PACK
OF CARDS SHOOTS INTO THE AIR AND COMES
FLUTTERING DOWN UPON HER...

WAKE UP!

WAKE UP, **ALICE DEAR!**

WHY, WHAT A **LONG SLEEP** YOU'VE HAD!

OH, I'VE HAD SUCH A **CURIOUS DREAM**...

AFTER ALICE HAS TOLD HER SISTER ALL ABOUT HER EXTRAORDINARY EXPERIENCE...

IT *WAS* A **CURIOUS** DREAM, DEAR, CERTAINLY...

...BUT NOW LET'S GO **HOME** FOR **TEA**, IT'S GETTING **LATE**.

The Story of
ALICE IN WONDERLAND

Alice's Adventures in Wonderland was written by Lewis Carroll in the early 1860s and soon became one of the most well-loved books in history.

Carroll, whose real name was Charles Lutwidge Dodgson, was born in 1832 in Cheshire, England, the son of a curate. He was educated at home until he was eleven years old and was a keen reader.

Lewis Carroll

In 1850, he attended Oxford University where he displayed a talent for mathematics. He was a member of his father's old college, Christ Church, and was to remain there in various roles for the rest of his life.

Dodgson had always enjoyed writing poems and short stories. His pieces, which were mostly humorous, soon began to appear in local and national magazines. In 1856, the romantic poem, *Solitude*, became his first work to be published under the pseudonym Lewis Carroll when it was printed in *The Train* magazine.

In the same year, Dodgson became friends with the recently appointed Dean of Christ Church, Henry Liddell, and his young family. Dodgson would often take Liddell's children on boating trips on the river Isis. It was during one such excursion, in July, 1862, in the company of Dodgson's friend Robinson Duckworth, that the seeds of Alice's adventures were sown.

Alice Liddell

In the course of the journey, Dodgson told Lorina, Alice and Edith Liddell a story about a girl named Alice who goes on a fantastic adventure. The three sisters were delighted by the tale and 10-year-old Alice Liddell asked Dodgson to write it down for her.

It was over two years later, just before Christmas 1864, that he presented her with *Alice's Adventures Under Ground*, a handwritten version of the story, complete with his own illustrations. In the dedication, Dodgson described it as 'A Christmas Gift to a Dear Child in Memory of a Summer's Day'.

For many years it was assumed that Alice Liddell was the inspiration for the title character, but Dodgson later denied that Alice was based on any real child. However, it is fair to assume that she was at least responsible for the character's name, as many of the characters in the story have links to Dodgson's friends. The Duck is a reference to Robinson Duckworth and the Lory and Eaglet to Lorina and Edith Liddell. The author himself is represented by the Dodo, as Dodgson suffered from a stammer which meant he often referred to himself as Dodo-Dodgson.

Before Dodgson presented Alice with the finished manuscript, his friend George MacDonald and his children had already read the unfinished version and their enthusiasm had given Dodgson the confidence to show it to the book publisher Macmillan.

They were keen to publish the story and, after rejecting alternative titles, such as *Alice Among the Fairies* and *Alice's Golden Hour*, *Alice's Adventures in Wonderland* finally appeared in print in 1865. In place of his own sketches, Dodgson had asked illustrator John Tenniel to supply the drawings for the book. These were to prove as enduring as the story itself and Tenniel's visualizations of characters such as the White Rabbit, the Hatter and the Queen of Hearts have become familiar versions.

John Tenniel's illustration of the White Rabbit

Although it received mixed reviews, the first edition of the book sold out quickly and it has never been out of print since. The surreal characters who talk nonsense, together with Dodgson's plays on words, are elements that appealed to both children and adults. Dodgson wrote a sequel,

Alice meets Tweedledum and Tweedledee in one of Tenniel's illustrations from *Through the Looking-Glass and What Alice Found There*

entitled *Through the Looking-Glass and What Alice Found There*, although it wasn't published until 1871. This book included *Jabberwocky*, a nonsense poem in a book discovered by Alice. The poem became almost as famous in its own right as the two Alice books. Dodgson later used some of the characters from *Jabberwocky* in his 1876 nonsense poem *The Hunting of the Snark*.

Despite his newfound fame and wealth, Dodgson remained as a teacher at Christ Church up to 1881 and lived there until his death from pneumonia on 14th January, 1898 during a visit to his sister's home in Guildford, Surrey.

Alice's Adventures in Wonderland has been translated into over 100 languages and adapted many times for plays, radio, film, TV and even ballet and opera. Its title is usually abbreviated to *Alice in Wonderland* and adaptations often include scenes from the sequel.

Russell Punter was born in Bedfordshire, England. From an early age he enjoyed writing and illustrating his own stories. He trained as a graphic designer at art college in West Sussex before entering publishing in 1987. He has written over sixty books for children, ranging from original stories to adaptations of classic novels.

Simona Bursi graduated with a Master's degree in cinematic animation from the Scuola del Libro art school in Urbino, Italy. She lived in Milan from 1997 to 2007 where she worked as both a character designer and also a storyboard, layout and animation artist for different production houses. She was a graphic artist and director of music videos for children and went on to create the *Bee-Bees* television series, broadcast in Italy and around the world. Since 2008, Simona has been living in Fano, Marche, working as an illustrator for a large number of Italian and foreign publishing houses.

Mike Collins has been creating comics for over 25 years. Starting on *Spider-Man* and *Transformers* for Marvel UK, he has also worked for DC, 2000AD and a host of other publishers. In that time he's written or drawn almost all the major characters for each company – *Wonder Woman, Batman, Superman, Flash, Teen Titans, X-Men, Captain Britain, Judge Dredd, Sláine, Rogue Trooper, Darkstars, Peter Cannon: Thunderbolt* and more. He currently draws a series of noir crime fiction graphic novels, *Varg Veum*. He also provides storyboards for TV and movies, including *Doctor Who, Sherlock, Igam Ogam, Claude, Hana's Helpline* and *Horrid Henry*.

Cover design: Matt Preston

Page 100: Photograph of Lewis Carroll © adoc-photos/Corbis/Getty Images
Page 101: Photograph of Alice Liddell © Getty Images / Sam Abell
Page 102: Illustration by John Tenniel © The Print Collector/Getty
Page 103: Illustration by John Tenniel © Universal History Archive/UIG/Getty Images